50 Flashcards $7.95

FlashCards

ALABAMA
High School

MATHEMATICS

**Preparing Students
for the AHSGE**

Printed in USA. Minimal packaging for a healthy environment.

HOLLANDAYS
Publishing Corporation

Given the geometric series $2^n + 1$, find the 5th, 6th, and 10th terms where n represents the term.

$5^{th} = 33$

$6^{th} = 65$

$10^{th} = 1025$

Choose the correct expression.
Prices for movie tickets are $5 for adults and $2 for children. Which expression represents the total cost for a group of a adults and c children to attend the theater?

a) $7 + a + c$ c) $5a + 2c$

b) $5a + c$ d) $7(a + c)$

How much would it cost for a family of one adult and two children to attend the theater?

c) $5a + 2c$

$5a + 2c =$ Total cost
$5(1) + 2(2) =$ Total cost
Total cost $= \$9$

It would cost $9 for one adult and two children to attend the theater.

Define absolute value.

Simplify:

a) $|3| = $ _____

b) $|-3| = $ _____

c) $3|-3| = $ _____

d) $\dfrac{|-3|}{3} = $ _____

An absolute value represents a value's distance from zero. This value is always positive.

a) 3   b) 3   c) 9   d) 1

Match the words and phrases with a math operation.

1) cut into parts
2) product
3) difference between
4) sum
5) quotient

6) times
7) decreased by
8) ratio
9) goes into
10) minus

4

1) Division

2) Multiplication

3) Subtraction

4) Addition

5) Division

6) Multiplication

7) Subtraction

8) Division

9) Division

10) Subtraction

Fraction	Decimal	Percent
		45%
	0.2	
4/5		
	0.36	
		70%
7/8		

5

Fraction	Decimal	Percent
$\frac{9}{20}$	0.45	45%
$\frac{1}{5}$	0.2	20%
$\frac{4}{5}$	0.8	80%
$\frac{9}{25}$	0.36	36%
$\frac{7}{10}$	0.7	70%
$\frac{7}{8}$	0.875	87.5%

Mr. Houston drove 60 miles in
1¼ hours. Answer the following
questions about Mr. Houston's trip.

a) What formula can you use to find Mr.
   Houston's speed?

b) Mr. Houston's average speed was _____
   miles per hour.

c) At the same speed, how far will
   Mr. Houston travel in 3 hours?

a) Distance = rate × time

b) Distance = rate × time
60 = rate × 1.25
$60 ÷ 1.25$ = rate
rate = 48 miles per hour

c) $48 × 3 = 144$ miles

State the slope and y-intercept for the following equations.

a) $y = \dfrac{2}{3}x - 1$

b) $y = -\dfrac{1}{2}x + 4$

7

a) slope $= \dfrac{2}{3}$, y-intercept $= -1$

b) slope $= -\dfrac{1}{2}$, y-intercept $= 4$

Find two positive numbers
with a product of 120 and a
difference of 2.

$$x\,y = 120$$
$$x - y = 2$$

$$x = y + 2$$
$$(y + 2)(y) = 120$$
$$y^2 + 2y - 120 = 0$$
$$(y + 12)(y - 10) = 0$$
$$y = -12, 10\text{ ; -12 is not positive}$$
$$y = 10\text{; therefore, } x = 12$$

The numbers are 12 and 10

Similar Triangles
$\triangle$ ABC $\sim$ $\triangle$ XYZ

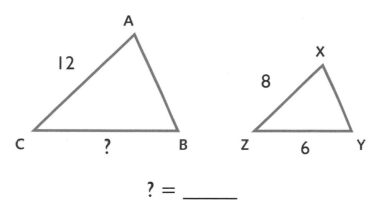

? = _____

9

Similar triangles have sides that are in proportion to each other.

Cross multiply to solve.

$$\frac{8}{12} = \frac{6}{?}$$

$? = 9$

Given the function, state the domain and the range.

a) $f(x) = 2x + 1$, with

x	y
0	1
-3	-5
2	5

b) $f(x) = x - 1$

c) $f(x) = x^2 + 1$

a) Domain: 0, -3, 2 **Range:** 1, -5, 5

b) Domain: any real number; $\{x: x$ is any real number$\}$
Range: any real number; $\{y: y$ is any real number$\}$

c) Domain: any real number; $\{x: x$ is any real number$\}$
Range: positive numbers greater than or equal to one; $\{y: y \geq 1\}$

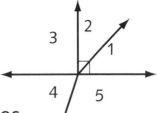

1) Define complementary angles.

2) Name a pair of complementary angles.

3) Define supplementary angles.

4) Name a pair of supplementary angles.

5) m∠ ___ + m∠ ___ + m∠ ___ = 180°

6) ∠1, ∠2 and ∠4 are _____ angles.

7) ∠5 is a/an _____ angle.

11

1) Two angles whose sum is 90°

2) $\angle 1$ and $\angle 2$

3) Two angles whose sum is 180°

4) $\angle 4$ and $\angle 5$

5) $\angle 1$, $\angle 2$ and $\angle 3$

6) acute

7) obtuse

Find the missing values in the proportions:

1) $\dfrac{3}{7} = \dfrac{x}{21}$

2) $\dfrac{2}{3} = \dfrac{x}{27}$

3) $\dfrac{4}{9} = \dfrac{12}{x}$

1) 9

2) 18

3) 27

1) Define and tell how to find the slope of line *l*.

  a) from the graph   **b)** from the equation

2) Define and tell how to find the y-intercept of the line.

  a) from the graph   **b)** from the equation

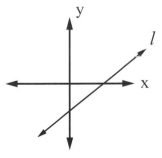

13

1) a) Pick two points on the line. Count the vertical distance (rise) and the horizontal distance (run) between the two points. Slope = rise ÷ run

   b) Convert the equation to slope-intercept form. Equation: $y = mx + b$; m is the slope

2) a) The point where the line crosses the y-axis is the y-intercept.

   b) Convert the equation to slope-intercept form. Equation: $y = mx + b$; b is the y-intercept

A) Define a function in terms of the domain and range.

B) State the domain and range described by this set: (0, 1) (-3, -5) (2, 5)

C) Given $f(x) = 2x + 1$, find:

$f(5)$

$f(-1)$

14

A) A function is a rule or correspondence between two sets, the domain and the range.
- The rule assigns each member of the domain to exactly one member of the range.
- Each member in the range must be assigned to at least one value in the domain.

B) Domain: -3, 0, 2   Range: -5, 1, 5

C) $f(5) = 2(5) + 1 = 11$
$f(-1) = 2(-1) + 1 = -1$

Given: $a \parallel b$

Use the figure to identify the following pairs of angles:

1) corresponding angles

2) alternate interior angles

3) alternate exterior angles

4) supplementary angles

5) Line c is called what?

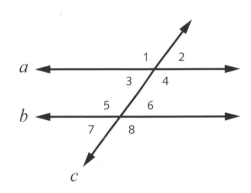

1) ∠1 and ∠5; ∠3 and ∠7;
∠2 and ∠6; ∠4 and ∠8

2) ∠3 and ∠6; ∠4 and ∠5

3) ∠1 and ∠8; ∠2 and ∠7

4) ∠3 and ∠5; ∠4 and ∠6;
∠1 and ∠3; ∠1 and ∠2, etc.

5) Transversal

Define:

1) mean   **2)** median

3) mode   **4)** range

5) The first three terms are referred to as

_____.

6) Which measure of central tendency is affected most by extremes in data?

1) The mean is the arithmetic average of a set of numbers.

2) After arranging the data values in order, the median is the middle value.

3) The mode is the value or values that occur most often in a data set.

4) The range is the distance between the highest and lowest values in a data set.

5) measures of central tendency

6) mean

Simplify.

1) $8x - 3y + 6 \cdot x \div 3 \cdot 4$

2) $\dfrac{(3x^2) - y^2 - 3x}{x}$

17

1) $16x - 3y$

2) $-y^2$

Simplify using the laws of exponents.

a) $(2xy)^0$

b) $\left(\dfrac{4x^{10}}{6y}\right)^2$

c) $(12a^3z^{11})(5a^2z^{-10}y^4)$

d) $\dfrac{15w^{20}x^{10}y^5}{25w^{25}x^5y^6}$

e) $(3x^2y)^2 + (7xz^3)^2$

a) 1

b) $\dfrac{4x^{20}}{9y^2}$

c) $60a^5zy^4$

d) $\dfrac{3x^5}{5w^5y}$

e) $9x^4y^2 + 49x^2z^6$

Beth is going to paint the floor of her
L-shaped swimming pool.

How many square feet of paint will
Beth apply?

What is the volume of her pool
if it averages 5 ft deep?

8'

8'

10'

8'

19

Beth will need 208 ft^2 of paint.

The volume of the pool is 1040 ft^3.

1) Sale prices are calculated by taking a percent off the original price. If an item is on sale for 20% off the original price, the sale price represents what percent of the original price?

2) The original price of a book was $25.00, but it is on sale for 30% off. How much does the book cost?

1) 80%

2) $17.50

1) At $5.75 per hour, how many hours would Dan need to work to earn $161.00?

2) Michael earns $6.50 per hour washing cars. Last week he worked 32 hours and received $72.00 in tips. How much money did he earn last week?

21

1) 28 hours

2) $280.00

Rewrite each sentence as a mathematical expression. Let x = weekly pay.

1) I can earn as much as $60.00 this week.

2) I am working full time next week, so I will earn more than $60.00.

1) $x \leq \$60.00$

2) $x > \$60.00$

The teacher has a sack filled with candy bars. He has 10 Chocos, 5 Mint Cups, 8 Twinbars, and 7 Peanut Clusters. What is the probability that a student will pick each candy bar below?

1) Chocos
2) Mint Cups
3) Twinbars
4) Peanut Clusters

1) 10/30 = 1/3

2) 5/30 = 1/6

3) 8/30 = 4/15

4) 7/30

Simplify:

1) -4×3

2) $-8 \div 2$

3) 3×-2

4) $25 \div 5$

5) -6×-3

6) When multiplying and/or dividing positive and negative numbers, if both numbers have the same sign, the answer is _____; however, if the two numbers have different signs, the answer is _____.

24

1) - 12

2) - 4

3) - 6

4) 5

5) 18

6) positive; negative

Probability

1) Describe a situation where probabilities are added.

2) Describe a situation where probabilities are multiplied.

25

1) When two events cannot both happen, they are mutually exclusive. The probability of either happening is the sum of the probability of each event happening.

2) If two events are independent, the probability of both events happening is the product of the probability of each event happening.

Give an algebraic expression for the following:

1) The value of x dimes and y nickels

2) The perimeter of a parallelogram with sides a and b

3) The average of c, d and e

4) The area of a rectangle with length (t) and width (u)

1) $0.10x + 0.05y$

2) $2a + 2b$

3) $(c + d + e) \div 3$

4) $(t)(u)$

Direct Variation

1) Describe direct variation.

2) Give a real world example of a direct variation problem.

1) If two variables have the same rate or ratio regardless of their values, they have a direct variation relationship.

You can say that "y varies directly with x" *or* "y varies directly as x."

Equation: $y = kx$ or $\dfrac{y}{x} = k$, where k is constant.

Example: $y = 8x$; the equation is a line.

2) a) John earns \$8 per hour. His gross earnings vary directly with the number of hours that he works.

b) The amount of interest earned on a savings account varies directly with the account's balance.

Emily's wages for a 15 hour work week increased by $6.75. Before the raise, she was earning $7.80 per hour. What is her new hourly wage?

28

$8.25

Simplify.

1) $\sqrt{25}$

2) $\sqrt{200}$

3) $\sqrt{72x^2y^3z^5}$

1) 5

2) $10\sqrt{2}$

3) $6xyz^2\sqrt{2yz}$

1) What methods can you use to solve a system of equations?

2) Solve the system of linear equations by any method.
$$x + y = 10$$
$$x - y = 6$$

30

1) • Graphing
   • Substitution to eliminate a variable
   • Linear combination
     (add/subtract/multiply/divide)
   • Matrices

2) (8,2)

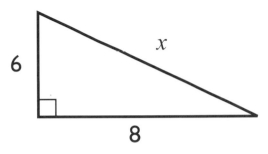

6

x

8

1) Solve for x. Use the Pythagorean
Theorem: $a^2 + b^2 = c^2$

2) The Pythagorean Theorem only applies to
which specific figures?

31

1) $8^2 + 6^2 = x^2$

$64 + 36 = x^2$

$100 = x^2$

$10 = x$

2) The Pythagorean Theorem only applies to right triangles.

1) When two triangles are similar, corresponding angles are _____ and corresponding sides are _____.

2) When two triangles are congruent, corresponding angles are _____ and corresponding sides are_____.

1) congruent; proportional

2) congruent; congruent

1) What is the sum of the measures of the interior angles of a triangle?

2) What is the area of this triangle?

3) What is the perimeter of this triangle?

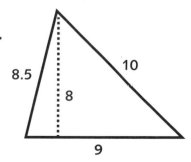

8.5

10

8

9

1) $180°$

2) The area of the triangle is 36 square units.

3) 27.5 units

Mark has scored 90, 85, and 79 on his math tests. What would he need to score on his next test to have a mean score of 88?

$$\frac{90 + 85 + 79 + x}{4} = 88$$

$$90 + 85 + 79 + x = 352$$

$$90 - 90 + 85 - 85 + 79 - 79 + x = 352 - 90 - 85 - 79$$

$$x = 98$$

Explain how to find the volume of a prism and cylinder.

To find the volume of a cylinder or prism, first find the area of the base. A prism has a two-dimensional figure (i.e., square, rectangle, triangle, or any regular polygon) as a base, and a cylinder has a circular base. Then multiply the area of the base by the height.

1) What is the volume of each figure?

2) What is the surface area of each?

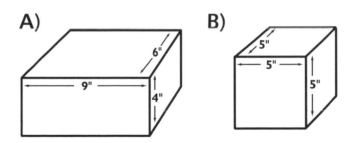

A)

B)

1) A) 216 inches^3
   B) 125 inches^3

2) A) 228 inches^2
   B) 150 inches^2

Give the following formulas and facts about the circle:

1) Define the diameter.
2) Define the radius.
3) Define the circumference.
4) The formula for the area is _____.
5) The formula for circumference is _____.
6) If d = 16, A = ___.

1) Diameter is the length of a straight line that passes through the center of a circle and connects two points on the circumference.

2) Radius is the distance from the center of a circle to any point on the circumference (the perimeter).

3) Circumference is the distance around a circle.

4) πr^2

5) $2\pi r$ or πd

6) 64π units^2

1) Using the distance formula, find the length of the segment between points A and B.

Point A: (-7, -4)

Point B: (9, 3)

2) Given points A and B, find the coordinates of the midpoint of $\overline{AB}$.

1) $\sqrt{(-7-9)^2+(-4-3)^2}$

$-16^2 + -7^2 = 305$

$\sqrt{305} \approx 17.46$ units

(9,3)

(-7,-4)

x

y

2) $\left(\dfrac{-7+9}{2}, \dfrac{-4+3}{2}\right)$

$\left(1, -\dfrac{1}{2}\right)$

Solve:

a) $3x - 2x + 5 = 15 - 3$

b) $3(x - 2) + 1 = 2x - 5$

c) $\dfrac{3x + 1}{5} = 3$

a) $3x - 2x + 5 = 15 - 3$

$x + 5 = 12$

$x + 5 - 5 = 12 - 5$

$x = 7$

b) $3(x + 2) + = 2x - 5$

$3x - 6 + 1 = 2x - 5$

$3x - 2x - 5 + 5 = 2x - 2x - 5 + 5$

$x = 0$

c) $\dfrac{3x + 1}{5} = 3$

$3x + 1 - 1 = 15 - 1$

$3x = 14$

$x = \dfrac{14}{3}$

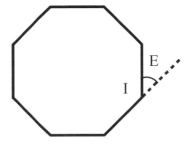

'A convex polygon has 8 sides.

a) Find the measure of the exterior angle E.

b) Find the measure of the interior angle I.

c) Find the sum of the interior angles.

40

a) $E = \dfrac{360}{8} = 45$

b) $I = 180 - 45 = 135$

c) $135 \cdot 8 = 1080$

The formula for finding the sum of interior angles is:

$$S = (N - 2)180$$
(where N = # of sides.)

Find the domain and range for
the following line segment.

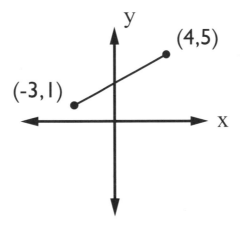

Domain: $\{x: -3 \le x \le 4\}$

Range: $\{y: 1 \le y \le 5\}$

Solve for x.
Find the value of the vertical angles.

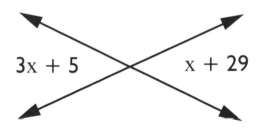

$3x + 5$ $x + 29$

42

$$3x + 5 = x + 29$$
$$2x = 24$$
$$x = 12$$

$$3(12) + 5 = 41°$$

Graph the following:

a) $x = 2$

b) $y = -2$

c) $y = (-\frac{1}{2})x + 2$

d) $3x - y = -1$

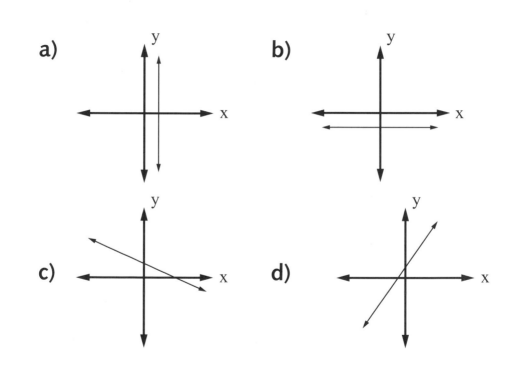

Solve and graph on a number line graph.

1) $x - 3 > 5$ or $2x + 7 \leq 5$

2) $x + 3 > -2$ and $4x + 5 \leq 1$

1) $x > 8$ or $x \leq -1$

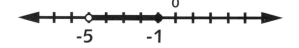

2) $x > -5$ and $x \leq -1$

Solve the quadratic equations by factoring.

1) $9x^2 - 16 = 0$

2) $x^2 - 5x = -6$

3) $2x^2 = 7x + 15$

4) $5x^2 - 6x = 0$

5) $(x^2 + 2x) + (5x + 10) = 0$

1) $x = \pm\dfrac{4}{3}$

2) $x = 2, x = 3$

3) $x = 5, x = -\dfrac{3}{2}$

4) $x = 0, x = \dfrac{6}{5}$

5) $x = -5, x = -2$

Find the greatest common factor (GCF).

1) $24x^2$ and $16x$

2) $2x^2y^3z$ and $5x^3y^2z$

3) $x^2 + 5x + 6$ and $x^2 - 9$

1) $8x$

2) x^2y^2z

3) $x + 3$

Which represents a function?

1) **a.**

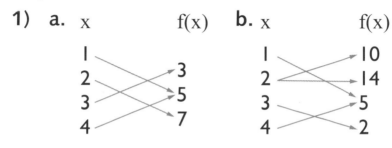

x	f(x)
1	3
2	5
3	7
4	

b.

x	f(x)
1	10
2	14
3	5
4	2

2) **a.**

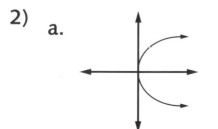

b.

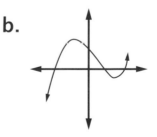

1) a
2) b

Factor completely.

1) $6x - 10y + 4z$

2) $3x^2 - 3$

3) $x^2 + 5x + 6$

4) $2x^2 - 7x - 15$

1) $2(3x - 5y + 2z)$

2) $3(x - 1)(x + 1)$

3) $(x + 2)(x + 3)$

4) $(x - 5)(2x + 3)$

Solve. Express the answer as a number line.

1) $3(x - 1) \geq 2(x + 3) + 3$

2) $5k - 2(k + 4) - 1 < 0$

3) $-12 \leq 3x - 3 < 15$

1) $x \geq 12$

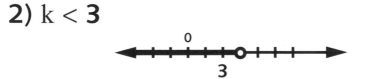

2) $k < 3$

3) $-5 \leq x < 4$

Solve the system of equations by graphing.

$$x + y = 5$$

$$x - y = 3$$

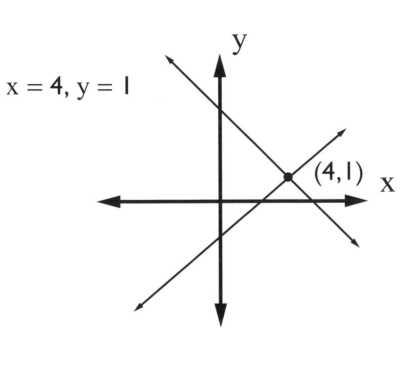

$x = 4, y = 1$

(4,1)

Dear Parents,

Here's how to use these flashcards to help your child prepare for the **Alabama Mathematics AHSGE:**

- Use the flashcards regularly. Practice 15-30 minutes each night for several weeks before the test.

- Make a checkmark on a flashcard each time your child answers that card correctly. After several sessions, look for flashcards with no (or few) checkmarks. Discuss these with your child and seek help from the teacher for these skills.

- Discuss each problem. Provide real life examples or talk about the steps your child needs to take to solve the problem.

- Read the advice to students on the reverse side of this card and urge your child to follow it.

US $7.95

ISBN 0-9753239-2-X

50795

9 780975 322390

Dear Student,
Here are some ideas to
help you on the
**Alabama Mathematics
AHSGE:**

• **Use the tools provided.** A calculator and
formulas can be used on test day. Use the
formulas to set up problems. Estimate the answer
and then use the calculator to solve all problems.

• **Draw and label figures.** If you must answer a
geometry problem about a triangle, draw and
label the triangle to help visualize the problem.

• **Answer all questions.** Difficult and easy problems
are mixed on the test. Don't give up if one
problem is very difficult.

• **Take your time and check your work.**

• **Solve problems by reading carefully.** Look for
key words and make sure you complete all steps
of a problem before choosing an answer.

• **Look for the three representations of pi:** π, pi,
and p. On the test, use 3.14 for pi.

**Remember to study your Flashcards for
15-30 minutes every day for
a few weeks before the test.**

©2004
Hollandays
Publishing
Corporation

6

7 14717 14101